E
398
Sew

C.2a

Sewall, Marcia
The World turned up-
side down . . .

DATE DUE			

Olympia
806

THE WORLD TURNED UPSIDE DOWN

AN OLD PENNY RHYME

ADAPTED AND ILLUSTRATED BY MARCIA SEWALL

BOSTON   The Atlantic Monthly Press   NEW YORK

FIRST EDITION

LIBRARY OF CONGRESS CATALOGING-IN-PUBLICATION DATA

Sewall, Marcia.
    The world turned upside down.

    Summary: An illustrated version of a traditional "penny rhyme" describing some unusual sights.
    1. Nursery rhymes. 2. Children's poetry.
[1. Nursery rhymes]   I. Title.
PZ8.3.S479Wo   1986   398'.8   85-20015
ISBN 0-87113-053-X

DNP

Published simultaneously in Canada

PRINTED IN JAPAN

Here you may see what's very rare,
       the world turned upside down;
Watch dog and ox some music make
       while cat rides hog to town.

To see a farmer feed his hog
is no news;
But to see a hare run after a dog
is strange indeed!

To see a good boy read his book

is no news;

But to see a goose roasting a cook

is strange indeed!

To see two ladies drinking tea

is no news;

But to see a bird shoot a man in a tree

is strange indeed!

To see a gardener gather a salad

is no news;

But to hear an ass singing a ballad

is strange indeed!

To see a haymaker using his rakes
is no news;
But to see a bear making plum cakes
is strange indeed!

To see a young girl wash her dog

is no news;

But to see a cat riding a hog

is strange indeed!

To see a farmer picking corn
is no news;
But to hear an ox blowing his horn
is strange indeed!

To see a bird pecking at fruit
is no news;
But to see a dog playing the flute
is strange indeed!

To see a cat chase after a mouse
is no news;
But to see a rat building a house
is strange indeed!

To see a dog baiting a bull

is no news;

But to see a ram spinning wool

is strange indeed!

To see a cart pulled by a goat

is no news;

But to see a hog rowing a boat

is strange indeed!

To see a cat drink milk from a pan
is no news;
But to see a hen gather eggs from a lamb
is strange indeed!

To see a man fish from a boat
is no news;
But to see a ram knitting a coat
is strange indeed!

To see a highbred horse go prancing
is no news;
But to see a cat fiddling and mice all dancing
is strange indeed!